This book belongs to:

. . . .

. . . .

. . . .

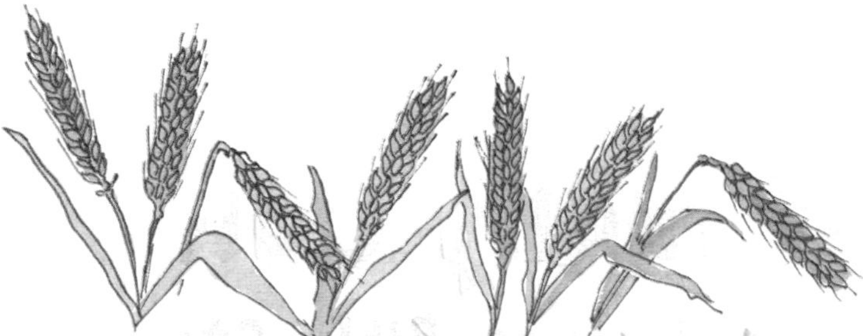

Joseph's Coat of Many Colours

and other Bible Stories

Retold by Gaby Goldsack
Illustrated by John Dillow

Language consultant: Betty Root

ISBN 1-84461-136-1

Marks and Spencer p.l.c.
PO Box 3339, Chester CH99 9QS
www.marksandspencer.com

Copyright © Exclusive Editions 2004

Printed in China

Joseph's Coat of Many Colours

and other Bible Stories

Contents

Helping your Child to Read

Learning to read is an exciting challenge for most children. From a very early age, sharing story books with children, talking about the pictures and guessing what might happen next are all very important parts of the reading experience.

Sharing reading

Set aside a regular quiet time to share reading with younger children, or to be on hand to encourage older children as they develop into independent readers.

First Readers are intended to encourage and support the early stages of learning to read. They present well-loved stories that children will happily listen to again and again. Familiarity helps children to identify some of the words and phrases.

When you feel your child is ready to move on a little, encourage them to join in so that you read the story aloud together. Always pause to talk about the pictures. The easy-to-read speech bubbles in **First Readers** provide an excellent 'joining-in' activity. The bright, clear illustrations and matching text will help children to understand the story.

Building confidence

In time, children will want to read *to* you. When this happens, be patient and give continual praise. They may not read all the words correctly, but children's substitutions are often very good guesses.

The repetition in each book is particularly helpful for building confidence. If your child cannot read a particular word, go back to the beginning of the sentence and read it together so the meaning is not lost. Most importantly, do not continue if your child is tired or simply in need of a change.

Reading aloud

The next step is to ask your child to read aloud to you. This does require patience and perseverance. Remember to give lots of encouragement and praise.

Together with other simple stories, **First Readers** will ensure that children will find reading an enjoyable and rewarding experience.

Joseph's Coat of Many Colours

GENESIS: 3-7

Jacob lived in Canaan.

He had twelve sons.

He loved Joseph and Benjamin best.

He gave Joseph a coat of many colours.

Joseph's brothers were cross.

Joseph had a dream. In his dream he was very important. He told his brothers the dream.

"Your corn bowed down before my corn," he said.

Your corn bowed down.

He thinks we will bow down before him!

The brothers were cross.

"He thinks we will bow down before him," they said.

They decided to get rid of Joseph.

The brothers went into the desert.

They took Joseph's coat.

Then they threw Joseph in a pit.

Some men came by on camels.

They were on the way to Egypt.

The brothers sold Joseph to the men.

Joseph was a slave.

The brothers
put blood on Joseph's coat.
They told Jacob that a wild
animal had killed Joseph.
Jacob was very sad.

I am
very sad.

In Egypt Joseph was sold to a man.
The man was his master.
Joseph was his slave.

The King's Dream

GENESIS: 39-41

Joseph was a good slave. His master
liked Joseph.

He put Joseph in charge of all
the other slaves.

I am in charge!

But his master's wife did not like Joseph.

She told lies about Joseph.

His master was sad.

He put Joseph in prison.

There were two other men in prison.

One man had a dream.

He told Joseph his dream.

God told Joseph the
meaning of the
dream.

One day, the King of Egypt had a dream.
He saw seven thin cows and seven fat cows.
The seven thin cows ate the seven fat cows.
The King sent for Joseph. He wanted
Joseph to tell him the meaning of the
dream. God told Joseph the meaning
of the dream.

"There will be lots of food
for seven years," said Joseph.
"Then there will be no food
for the next seven years."

The King liked Joseph.
He put Joseph in charge of the food.

21

No Food

GENESIS: 42-47

Joseph saved lots of food for seven years.
Then there was no food for the next
seven years.
Everyone came to Joseph to ask for food.
Joseph's brothers came to Egypt.

The brothers bowed down before Joseph.
Just like the corn sheaves had bowed in
Joseph's dream.

They asked him for food.
They did not know who he was.
But Joseph knew them.
Joseph gave them food.

Joseph hid a silver cup in a sack.

He gave the sack to Benjamin.

The guards found the

silver cup. The brothers

were scared.

"Benjamin must stay," said Joseph.

"Let me stay in his place," said another

brother.

Joseph was happy because he could see his brothers were good.

He told them who he was.

Joseph hugged his brothers. He told them to bring his father, Jacob, to Egypt. So Jacob and his family came to live in Egypt with Joseph. Jacob was very happy to find his lost son.

They lived happily for many years.

Read and Say

How many of these words can you say?
The pictures will help you. Look back in
your book and see if you can find the
words in the story.

corn

coat

cup

cow

slave

pit

sack

Joseph

king

Titles in this series, subject to availability: